Magic Mates
and the
Battle of the Bullies

Jane West

RISING★STARS

Rising Stars UK Ltd.
22 Grafton Street, London W1S 4EX
www.risingstars-uk.com

The right of Jane West to be identified as the author of this work
has been asserted by her in accordance with the Copyright, Design
and Patents Act 1988.

Published 2008

Text, design and layout © Rising Stars UK Ltd.

Cover design: Button plc
Illustrator: Stik, Bill Greenhead for Illustration
Text design and typesetting: Andy Wilson
Publisher: Gill Budgell
Editor: Jane Wood

British Library Cataloguing in Publication Data.
A CIP record for this book is available from the British Library

ISBN: 980 1 84680 330 7

Printed in the UK by CPI Bookmarque, Croydon, CR0 4TD

Mixed Sources
Product group from well-managed
forests and other controlled sources
www.fsc.org Cert no. TT-COC-002227
© 1996 Forest Stewardship Council

Contents

Extras!

Meet the Magic Mates

The Magic Mates are best friends –
but that doesn't mean they're all alike.

Name: 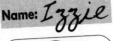 *Izzie*

The sporty one: can climb trees,
surf and take on the boys
at their own game – and win.

Travels by: running!

Loves: trendy tracksuits, open skies
and sandy beaches.

Hates: standing still.

Name: *Meena*

The girly one: uses her mobile
for networking and planning
her social life.

Travels by: Mum's car (her personal
chauffeur).

Loves: pink and her Magic Mates.

Hates: breaking a nail.

Name: *Ginger*

The ginger one: you don't wanna mess with this feisty gal – the Kung Fu and quick quip queen!

Travels by: push-scooter.

Loves: Jackie Chan and her Magic Mate pals.

Hates: nail extensions.

Name: Jo

The clever one: uses her brains and quick wit to talk her way out of trouble. Sometimes she's a bit too quick.

Travels by: bicycle and is designing a pair of motorised rollerblades.

Loves: Jacqueline Wilson, Cathy Cassidy and Albert Einstein.

Hates: being called 'geek', 'nerd', 'swot' or 'boffin'.

Name: Ellie

The fashion-conscious one: can tell her Prada from her Asda and knows how to accessorise.

Travels by: limousine, of course! (But only in her dreams.)

Loves: shopping.

Hates: anything to do with getting dirty; anyone who upsets her Magic Mates.

Name: Yash

The funky punky one: the 'alternative' one of the gang who hugs trees, people and furry animals.

Travels by: skateboard.

Loves: having a good time.

Hates: bullies.

The Road Home

The Magic Mates are going home after school. They're talking about what they're doing tonight.

Izzie   I'm going swimming with my dad. You can all come with us if you like.

Yash   That sounds fun. Count me in!

Ellie   I can't. I've got a violin lesson.

Meena   I can't either. My little cousin
Mindy is coming over.
I'm looking after her.

Ginger   Swimming sounds fun but I've got
my Kung Fu class tonight.
I'm going for my blue belt.
I've been practising really hard,
so I hope I get it.

Jo   I wonder how they chose
the colours for each grade:
white for beginners, then yellow,
orange, green, blue, brown
and black when you're
really good.

Ellie   I don't know why they chose
brown. No one looks good
in brown.

As the Magic Mates turn the corner
they see a group of Year 9 girls
from St Pingpong High School.
They don't look friendly.

Girl 1   Oh look! It's some little babies from Year 6. Ahhh.

Girl 2   Primary school kids are so little. Don't they look sweet?

Girl 3   I wonder if the sweeties
have got any sweeties.

Girl 1   Give us your sweets.

Ginger   No way!

Girl 2   Did the gingernut say 'no'?

Girl 4   Nah. She wouldn't be so stupid.

Ginger   I said 'no' and I meant it.
We're not giving you our sweets.

Jo   And don't call her a 'gingernut'.

Girl 2   I'll call her what I like.

Jo   You can call her a Kung Fu
champion. Then you'd be right.

The two groups of girls stare
at each other. The girls from
St Pingpong's can see that
the Magic Mates aren't scared
of them and they go away.

Izzie   I can't stand bullies.

Yash   Me neither.

Ellie   I don't think they'll bother us again.

Jo   No. But they might pick on some younger children. We must stop them.

An Early Start

Jo has been thinking about how to
stop the bullies from St Pingpong's.
She's come up with a plan,
but she needs help. She sends
a text message to Ginger.

Hi Ginger! Meet
me b4 skool at
park.

Ginger arrives at the park. Jo is waiting for her with a serious look on her face.

Ginger   What's the matter?

Jo   We must do something about those St Pingpong's girls. They're bullies.

Ginger   I know, but I don't think they'll pick on the Magic Mates again.

Jo   No, but they'll pick on someone else. Bullies always do. We have to stop them.

Ginger   Izzie phoned me last night.
She's going to tell our teacher
about them.

Jo   That's a good plan.
But I have another idea.
Listen …

Jo explains her idea to Ginger.
It involves Ginger, planks of wood
and Meena's little cousin Mindy …

Ginger   Ha, ha, ha! That's so funny!
Do you think it will really work?

Jo   Yes. Bullies are cowards.
If they think someone
can stand up to them,
they'll leave them alone.

Ginger   OK. I'll text Meena and get Mindy to walk home from school with us. When the St Pingpong's girls see her in the park, they'll try and take her sweets.

Jo   I can't wait to see their faces when they see what Mindy can do!

Lessons in the Park

It's after school in the park. Jo is reading a book and Ginger is teaching Mindy some Kung Fu moves.

Ginger   Kung Fu isn't about learning to fight. It's about learning to defend yourself.

Mindy   But what if they're bigger than me?

Ginger   It doesn't matter. I can throw my dad and he weighs loads more than me.

Mindy   Wow! How do you do that?

Ginger   I use his speed and weight against him.

Mindy   I don't understand.

Ginger   Have you ever seen two dogs
           chasing each other in the park?

Mindy   Yes.

Ginger   A little dog isn't as fast
           or as strong as a big dog,
           but they can turn much
           more quickly and run away.
           Well, it's a bit like that.
           You can win against bigger,
           heavier people.

Jo   I saw a film where this small man
           beat lots of bigger men. He did
           lots of Kung Fu.

Ginger Yes, that's Jackie Chan.
           He's my favourite film star.
           He's amazing.

Jo   So with a bit of movie magic,
a bit of Kung Fu and Mindy,
we'll teach those St Pingpong's
girls they can't go around
bullying little kids.

Ginger   Quick! Let's get ready!
Here they come!

The Battle of the Bullies

Girl 1   There's only two of them now, and a little kid.

Girl 2   Bet they're not so brave now.

Girl 3   I bet they don't talk back this time!

Girl 4   Let's see if they've got any sweets.

Girl 1   Oi, you! Got any sweets?

Jo   Are you talking to me?
This is a book, not a bag
of sweets.

Ginger   I don't think they can tell
the difference. They've probably
never read a book.

Girl 2 It's the gingernut.
She thinks she's funny.

Ginger I think it's going to be
pretty funny if you try
and take Mindy's sweets.

Girl 3   What do you mean?

Ginger   Mindy doesn't like bullies.

Girl 4   So what?

Jo   I don't think you should mess with Mindy.

Mindy is looking very serious.
She doesn't like bullies at all.

Girl 1   Do we look stupid?

Ginger   Well, now you mention it …

Girl 2   Right! I'm having
that kid's sweets.

Jo   Mindy, show them
what you can do.

A piece of wood is resting across
two piles of bricks. Mindy walks up
to the piece of wood. She looks
like Ginger when she's doing
her Kung Fu.

Girl 1   What's she doing?

Ginger   She's just practising her Kung Fu.
All the children at our school
know Kung Fu.

Girl 2   I don't know anything
about that.

Jo   I think there are a lot of things
you don't know anything about.
Like being nice.

Mindy   Aeeieee!

Mindy Kung Fu chops the piece
of wood in half with her bare hand.
The girls from St Pingpong's
can't believe their eyes.

Girl 1   How did she do that?

Jo   I told you. All the children at our school know Kung Fu.

Ginger   I haven't been teaching Mindy for very long, but she's pretty good.

Girl 2   Let's get out of here!

Ginger Just before you go … we've told
our teacher about you.
Your headteacher will be
getting a phone call about you.
You're in big trouble.

Jo And you deserve everything
you get. You big bullies!

The girls from St Pingpong's run away.
Jo, Ginger and Mindy fall to the ground,
laughing.

A Bit of Showbiz Magic

Jo and Ginger are walking Mindy home.
They're all very pleased with their
afternoon's work.

Ginger   Do you think they'll guess
how we did it?

Jo   No. I think they're more worried
about what their headteacher
is going to do.

Ginger   Yes. She'll sort out those bullies.

Mindy   Can I show my mum that trick?

Jo   Yes, we'll show her
when we get you home.

Ginger   They'll never guess
we used balsa wood!

Jo   Yes, balsa looks like real wood,
           but it's so thin and light,
           you can almost tear it like paper.

Ginger Where did you get the idea
            to use balsa wood?

Jo   I was thinking about all the tricks
           and special effects that they use
           when they make films.
           Those bullies saw what we wanted
           them to see.

Ginger   So they thought Mindy
was chopping a great big
piece of wood in half,
when really …

Jo   It was as easy to tear as paper!

Ginger   That was a really good idea, Jo.

Jo   It wouldn't have worked
without Mindy. You were
really good.

Mindy   Thanks, Jo. It's been fun.
I won't be scared of bullies
any more. They're just
scaredy cats.

Ginger You were really good
at the Kung Fu, too.
Maybe your mum will let you
have lessons. It's not just boys
who do sports like Karate
and Judo and Kung Fu.

Jo But you don't need muscles
to beat bullies …

Ginger Just brains and some
Magic Mates!

About the Author

Like Ginger, Jane West enjoys watching films with the Kung Fu stars Bruce Lee and Jackie Chan.

Jane West:

- lives by the beach in Cornwall
- likes taking her dog Pip paddling in the sea
- loves bodyboarding
- has worked in an art gallery, a bookshop and a school.

Now she's a writer, and has had great fun writing about the Magic Mates. She hopes you liked reading about them.

What is Bullying?

- 👄 Name-calling.

- 👄 Telling lies that get you into trouble.

- ✊ Pushing, shoving, pinching, biting, spitting or hitting you.

- 🪙 Taking or hiding your things or your money.

- 🗑 Spoiling your stuff.

👄 Telling lies or spreading rumours about you.

👄 Telling other children not to be your friend.

☞ Threatening you: 'If you don't do what I say, I'll ...'

📞 Phoning you and being rude, or not speaking at all (silent calls).

💻 Sending rude texts or emails, or putting rude messages about you on the Internet.

41

What To Do ...

If you know someone who is being bullied ...
tell someone.

Bullies like it when no one tells on them
because then they can keep on bullying people.

Don't suffer in silence! Tell someone!

You can get lots of helpful
information from this website:
www.bullying.co.uk.

**Remember –
don't do a bully a favour
by keeping quiet.**

Joke Time

Why did the Kung Fu girl cross the road?

To break the board on the other side.

Why was the skeleton always left out of Kung Fu lessons?

Because he had no body to go with.

Kung Fu!

 Kung Fu is a Chinese martial art, which means a way of fighting. It goes back at least 3000 years.

 Kung Fu means 'achievement through great effort'. That's because it takes a lot of hard work to be really good at Kung Fu.

 Kung Fu is a form of self-defence. You learn how to defend yourself without using weapons.

 Bruce Lee, a Chinese-American actor, made Kung Fu famous through his films in the 1970s.

 Jackie Chan and Jet Li are both Chinese actors who have made Kung Fu popular in their films today.

 There are lots of other types of martial arts. Judo, Karate, Tai Chi and Kickboxing are all popular sports in the UK.

Never try to do Kung Fu moves without proper lessons. You could hurt yourself and the people around you.

Kung Fu Quiz

1 Is Kung Fu only done by
   Chinese people?

2 Does Kung Fu means 'the easy way'?

3 Who was the first actor to make
   Kung Fu famous?

4 Name two other martial arts.

5 Why shouldn't you do Kung Fu moves
   by yourself?

How did you score?

0–1 That's more Kung Poo than Kung Fu!

2–3 Not bad, but it's not Kung Fu.

4–5 Ker Pow! You're a Kung Fu queen!

Magic Mates

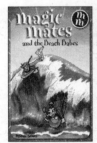   

RISING ★ STARS

Magic Mates books are available from most booksellers.

For mail order information
please call Rising Stars on 0871 47 23 010
or visit www.risingstars-uk.com